FANTASIES & OTHER REALITIES

The Pen & Ink Drawings
of
Nancy Chien-Eriksen
Text by Bruce C. Eriksen

A Wind Dance Publication

Additional copies of this
volume may be ordered from,
Wind Dance Publications
113 Rice Lane,
Larkspur, CA. 94939

A WIND DANCE PUBLICATION

ISBN 0-932473-00-8

Fantasy is the dream of our desires, it can be
joy and sadness together in a peaceful smile…

A momentary twinkle of the eye while the
world's routine continues on.

It is our minds in the process of inventing
and creating in a precious moment of freedom,

For fantasy and imagination shall always
provide the wings to the free-flying spirit of life.

With love,

Nancy Theen Eriksen

We dedicate this book to
our collectors who supported us,
our friends who encouraged us,
and our family who believed in us.

Special thanks to
Betty Hodson whose persistent
good advice and support was invaluable,

and to Diana Clardy
for her hard work and good cheer
throughout the task of
typesetting and design.

CONTENTS

Text by
Bruce C. Eriksen
unless otherwise noted.

Introduction

Art is first nature to Nancy Chien-Eriksen. She has always been naturally prolific. As a child she began drawing on any surface available. She used paper if she had it, but if she didn't, she would use newspapers, cloth, and at night even the walls next to her bed. That enthusiasum remains.

Her father was a Chinese diplomat and calligrapher, and her grandfather, also a calligrapher, was a scholar in the Royal Imperial Court of Peking. Art in such a family was revered, but in a scholastic family academics were the priority. It was not until college, after she had proven her scholastic ability, that the possibility of studying art occurred to her. With plans to study biological illustration she entered UCLA on a scholarship and eventually chose to specialize in art history. At age nineteen, she received a grant to study at the University of Padua, Italy, where she discovered excitement in the work of the Italian masters. As part of the program she was tutored at the Academy of Fine Arts in Venice in the same basic techniques used by the Renaissance artists. On holidays she frequented the great museums of Europe. Her natural Oriental background began to merge with her European education.

She continued to draw on anything available. As the impulse moved her she would sketch even on restaurant napkins, if they were the only papers handy. I saw many waiters in Italy react with delight to the gems she left at their tables. My mailman was also regularly entertained by the illustrations on the front and back of her letters to me. I soon found myself following her around, picking up the illustrations she left behind her. She was modestly unaware of how deeply her images affected those who saw them. Finally she began to keep her spontaneous images in small bound books. They wonderfully chronicled her impressions of the world as she moved through it. The people to whom she showed them would marvel at how much she could say with so few lines and a caption. I remember her saying, "Sometimes it is not how much one includes, but what is not included that is important. There has to be room for the viewer to participate in the art. An artist must know when to end as well as where to begin."

When Nancy finally began to show her work in public the response was instantaneous. She began by doing intricate pen and ink portraits for as little as one dollar, then she gradually introduced small freehand designs of her own fantasies. Those fortunate enough to buy those first fantasy drawings now value them as much as I do the "little treasures" I had collected. She went beyond the lines and color on the paper and communicated ideas.

Nancy's creatures each have their own unique intelligence and balance with nature. Her fantasy world parallels the positive hopes and dreams of perfection we all wish for—that is, a perfection made up of imperfections as well. They illustrate for us an ideal state of mind, a challenge for a fleeting moment of harmony that all of us can share.

1

Her unicorns portray truth and pureness of heart, while the dragons symbolize the raw but wisest forces of nature. In her artist's view of life, wild creatures become trusting friends, wizards interpret the mysteries of the universe, and men and women realize peace through acts of gentility and courage. To her nothing is more beautiful than for a creature to simply be itself.

These words can only alert you to the essence of Nancy's vision. Her medium is visual. With her artistry the lines she creates turn fantasies into realities that you and I can experience each in our own way.

UNICORNS

Wild and rare,
Young yet old,
Loving and free forever...

Unicorns

In our time the symbol of the Unicorn has illuminated a large portion of the consciousness of even those who doubt them to be a possibility. Their image appears everywhere. In some publications they are illustrated as wild horse-like beasts with brutal power. Other sources visualize them as creatures of entrancing delicate beauty. If a Unicorn never actually strode the earth in the flesh, then at least on some ephemeral plane, or in some timeless dimension, the Unicorn does exist.

Why The Unicorn?

"The Unicorn represents the free spirit of nature and perfection— ever beautiful and ever elusive.

"The Unicorn symbolizes the Joy of freedom and self discovery... generosity and pureness of heart...innocence.

"Together these qualities make up a wisdom that can no more be defined than the look in a Unicorn's eye.

"It is love and it is the gift of love."

—Nancy Chien-Eriksen

© NANCY CHIEN-ERIKSEN 84

The Silent Call

W e all have models of perfection. The places where we would like to go, the people we would like to know, and the person we would like to be, are made up of these ideals. Sometimes we embody all of these attributes into one image that represents magnificence and perfection. The Unicorn is such a symbol.

He stands erect and alert among the rushes, wading in an unknown cool forest stream. Autumn leaves begin their floating dance at his feet. His face is at once sweet and determined. His eyes...oh yes, his eyes are clear and deep. The flowing tresses of his mane and tail are like silk in the wind. His cloven hoof breaks the water noiselessly and sends ripples through the mirror of his reflection. Is it you or I who wishfully beckons? His horn of graceful spiraling ivory points the way of his attention. At any moment he may spring into motion and vanish into the thicket. But for the moment, he is the sight of a lifetime, and we dream to hear his Silent Call.

The Gift

At last she has found him.
Through faith alone she persisted
In the search for her ideal,
The perfect Unicorn.

In reverence she approaches him,
And he succumbs to her loving embrace.
She is filled with warmth
And a selfless desire
To give her devotion to him.

She offers in her young hand
A secret sweet,
And he accepts it
With sparkling trust in his eyes.

They will forever be enchanted
With a secret loving bond of friendship,
Itself its own most precious Gift.

The Return From the Sea

*E*ach one of us has looked at clouds and tried to imagine what animals we could see in the changing shapes. The sea is also able to play with our imagination. For centuries sailors have reported sightings of serpents, beasts, maidens with fish tails, and other exotic wonders. The next time you stand by an ocean shoreline and observe its relentless power and beauty, look closely. There might be more to see.

Peter Beagle, in his book *The Last Unicorn*, wrote of a sorcerer who lived in his castle high on a precipice overlooking the sea. The waves roared and slashed against the rocks. This man was so powerful and greedy that he conjured a spell that drove all of the Unicorns into the sea to become the foam of the waves.

But, as luck would have it, there was one last Unicorn. With the help of the friends she made on her quest, the spell was broken and the waters opened for the Return From the Sea.

The Unicorn of the Roses

*E*ach creature on this earth has its own unique way of moving. Often it is possible to tell something about that particular animal's character from the way it moves. For instance, the lion stalks, the horse prances, and the rabbit hops.

One creature walks so lightly, with steps so velvety smooth, that even leaves rarely rustle beneath its feet. So sweet and fragrant can the Unicorn be that perhaps it is true that a flower is born under its delicate feet wherever the unicorn spreads its enchantment.

13

The Unicorn Rests

*E*ven if the Unicorn didn't have a spiraling horn of flawless ivory or a mane which flows in silky shimmering tresses, its eyes would reveal its most worthy beauty...its pureness of heart.

The Unicorn has such inner tranquillity that its calm is contagious. When meandering through the forest, or cavorting across a meadow, the Unicorn notices the little things which combine to make life special. In such a moment, when the time is right, the air will have a stimulating spark. The plants will seem as fresh as if it had just rained, and the flowers will appear brilliant as if they had just opened their hearts. Even the mushrooms will look taller and plumper.

This is the moment when the Unicorn, sure that it is safe and alone, will lie upon the grass, throw back its head, and be one with nature. It is a rare person indeed who has witnessed this sight, because the slightest rustle in the grass, or the snap of the tiniest twig, would send the delicate creature wisely scurrying to the safety of the depth of the woods.

But, if the Unicorn senses that the person who is watching is pure of heart and has only the best of intentions, maybe, just maybe, it will linger a moment longer—reward in itself...from the Spirit of the Unicorn.

Untitled

One for your own imagination to create.

NANCY CHIEN-ERIKSEN '81

The New Unicorn

The existence of the Unicorn is rare and fragile. It depends on our belief to exist. What could be more precious than to imagine a baby Unicorn nestled beside its mother?

Perhaps the most wonderful quality of the Unicorn is that it amplifies our emotions. It enables us to feel more of what we ourselves are.

The mother Unicorn gives all of her warmth and nurturing to the world through the gift of her child. The baby feels safe as long as she is near, and as it grows the young one will have the wisest of guides in the ways of the world.

Rest assured that nearby the father stands alert to every sound and movement in the forest. He is ready with his experience and strength to protect his family. He is poised to meet any challenge to their safety. The mother can feel secure in this her special moment of tenderness with the baby Unicorn. Thus this new being portends the joy of new hope to an awakening world.

Rainbow Nymph

She is the Unicorn's constant companion.
Eternally young and spritely,
She sings of the amorous scents
Of wild flowers and spring.

Her kitten-like playfulness
And feline sensuousness
Are what attracts the Unicorn.
Men see her in the clouds of their longing,
Wishing they could have a companion so perfect.

But she resides in the furthest wood,
And requires more than amorous whimsy,
Before she would abandon her carefree life
As the Rainbow Nymph.

Midnight Ride

Not a soul knew. It was her secret. After everyone was asleep and only embers burned in the stove, Vanessa, still in her night dress, slipped out from under the covers of her bed and stole out the back door. Then she ran across the garden and entered the dark woods. She needed no lantern. The silhouette of the trees and the feel of the land on her bare feet told her the way. How well she knew it.

Once in the meadow, she raised her hands to her mouth and imitated the call of the night owl. At first there was silence, then a rustling followed by a steady stamping in the dark shadows. She signaled once more. Then, in answer, he stepped out into the moonlight. His white coat, stark against the night's background, gleamed mysteriously. With a gentle nodding of his head, he waved his single horn in a further signal to come forth.

In the moonshine her skin appeared white like his. She approached him quietly, embraced his lowered neck, then grabbing his mane she pulled herself onto his back. Shyrah! she whispered and the Unicorn leaped into motion. The trees of the forest blurred while her long hair trailed behind. They raced as free and long as the wind.

She rode and rode until time existed no more. Later that night, once again upon her bed, her mind still whirled from the private joy of her Midnight Ride.

23

The Unicorn Stream

E veryone has heard of the search for the Unicorn. But what of the Unicorn's search? If the Unicorn is attracted to truth and purity, then when he encounters such, what might he do?

Suppose two young women happen upon a crystal clear pool fed by a mountain stream. The day being hot with no one near, they shed their clothes and slip into the refreshing water. Once cool, one of the fair lasses climbs up to the bank and combs her long hair until it flows evenly in the air to dry. The other prefers to float in the calm water to gaze up into the patterns of branches and multi-colored leaves against an azure sky. Though they may have swum there before, there is a special energy this time. It is as if time stood still. Any care has fled with the breeze.

Hidden in the high growth is the Unicorn. It watches them with as much breathless caution as they might have watched him if they found him bathing. They don't know how close they are to a magical presence which might transform their lives, if they would be lucky enough to see him. How many times has he waited just out of view watching them?

How many times have possibilities been around the corner, aware of us and observant, awaiting discovery?

25

Unicorn In The Garden

A misty chill in the air was being warmed by the sun. The maiden breathed the freshness of the garden in the woods just after sunrise. She often strolled undisturbed then to hum her private songs aloud. She imagined wonderful scenes to accompany them. Singing them made her smile.

At the edge of an open glen she leaned against a tree and caressed its soft fuzzy bark. Suddenly, in the corner of her eye she saw a glow of blue white. It might have been a deer, so she turned very, very slowly to not frighten it away. But when her eyes met those of the creature's, she gasped silently. They were deeper and more beautiful than any she had ever seen before. They were like those of a buck but, instead of antlers, in the middle of its head was one spiraling horn. It was a Unicorn!

She stood as still as she could, not daring even to take a breath. She wanted the moment to last forever. It was as if one of her songs had come to life. The Unicorn lowered its head and nuzzled the newly blooming flowers near his cloven hooves. He was not afraid of her.

Dare she? She had to try. She might never have the chance again, so she made one very cautious step forward, her skirts rustling. The Unicorn raised its head, and again they were locked in a gaze. Softly she began to hum a tune. His stance seemed to ease, so she boldly took another step. Still the tall, glowing white creature did not move a muscle. His eyes drew her to him. Another step, then another...how close would he let her come, she wondered? Then she lifted her hand up towards him, so slowly that it was difficult to see it move. He shifted his weight back slightly in caution, but he did not flee. When her hand touched his quivering shoulder, he turned shyly and backed off, arching his neck with pride.

"Don't go," she whispered, while she took another step towards him. She blew him a kiss. It seemed to soften his stance, and to her amazement he lowered his horn at her feet. She touched the cool ivory horn. The Unicorn trusted her. Finally she drew herself up, took his warm muzzle into her gentle hands, and kissed it softly. She knew she would never be alone again now that she had met her Unicorn in the Garden.

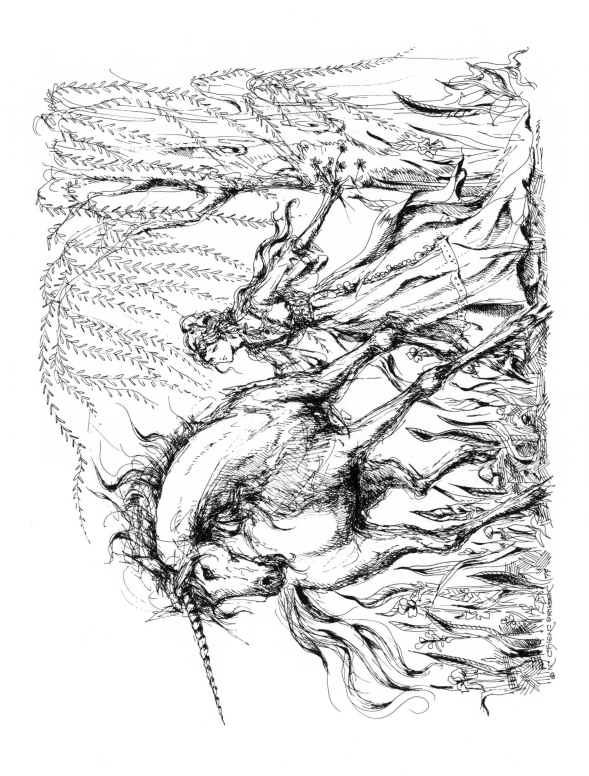

Unicorn Bouquet

This winter was especially chilly. Soliste and Printema had searched for many hours in vain for a unique gift for Queen Xandra's Birthday. Though the weather was bitter the king had suggested to them to find fresh blooms. They were loyal to the king and did not want to disappoint the Queen, so they dressed heavily and trekked out far beyond the castle walls to where it was cold and barren.

After searching for hours Soliste said to Printema, "It is hopeless, you know."

"Never give up hope." Printema encouraged her innocently. "If you have a dream, miracles can happen." Just as they spoke an unusual mist approached them. It seemed to be glowing.

"Look!" exclaimed Soliste. "What is that?"

"I-I don't know...but let's find out." suggested Printema.

Cautiously they stepped towards the mist. It seemed to grow larger as they came near, until it engulfed them in a strange warmth. All they could see was a soft grey-whiteness.

"Oh dear, what is happening?" wondered Soliste. Her voice shook with fright.

Then white on white, a form began to take shape from the mist. "It's a Unicorn!" exclaimed Printema in awe. With the sweetest of eyes the Unicorn looked at them, unafraid. "You...you are a miracle!" stuttered Soliste.

The Unicorn must have understood, for with a wink he touched his horn to the ground, and rich grasses suddenly appeared. Through the grass, shoots bearing flowers sprouted and bloomed before them in an array of colors.

The two were so happy that they shed their winter clothes and danced from flower to flower in the blessed warmth. As they picked the most beautiful ones, they decorated their hair and even placed a few in the Unicorn's mane. For the moment all was heaven as they frolicked in the newborn spring with their remarkable new friend.

"This is wonderful, but we must return to our King and Queen," Printema finally reminded the younger Soliste.

"Oh must we? It is so happy here," Soliste pleaded.

"Yes, it is, but we must remember our duty to Queen Xandra," Printema insisted.

Soliste sighed in resignation, and they quickly gathered up their flowers into a glorious bouquet. "Our King and Queen will certainly love these," she declared.

"May we see you again, dearest Unicorn?" Printema asked shyly.

The Unicorn's eye twinkled in a way that seemed to agree, and he bowed his horn to them. They each caressed it as a sad farewell. Immediately the surrounding grass and flowers disappeared. When the mist faded away once more, they found themselves suddenly in front of the castle. As they entered, they exchanged a knowing wink, while all of the people of the castle marvelled with delight at their magical Unicorn Bouquet.

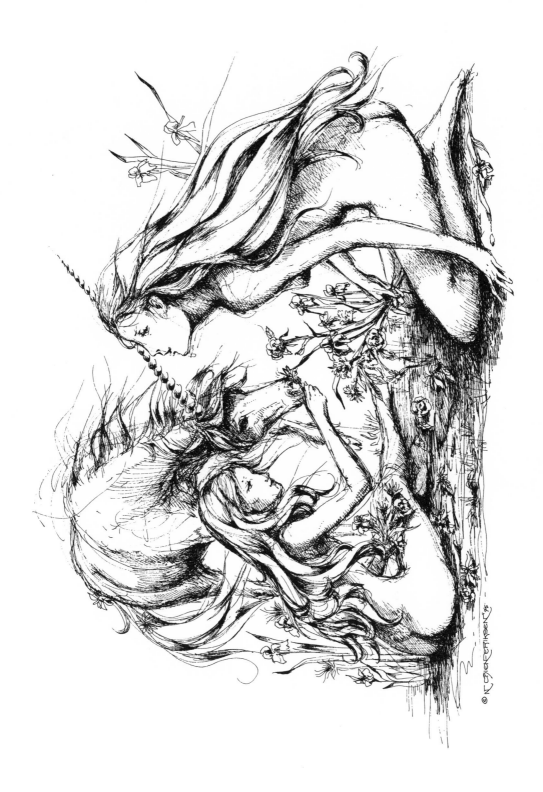

Rainbow Dream

Being a princess, Scylla had a great many responsibilites. Each week she met with her father's council, managed daily receptions, and passed judgment on many important matters. She was very accustomed to her duties, and she did her best to expand her abilities. Her father and mother were very, very proud for they felt that even a son could not have done better than the devoted Scylla.

It seemed, however, that the smiling princess was appearing pale and weary lately. She denied her fatigue and continued her work. One evening, after a particularly arduous day at the council, Scylla collapsed upon the stone floor. Her father cried out and carried her to a chaise in the next chamber. She breathed but seemed wan and nearly lifeless.

She lay unmoving for a long time when an old sorceress appeared. The distraught king allowed her to approach the girl. The old woman examined her thoughtfully, then bent over to whisper a mysterious chant in the princess' ear. With strange words that no one else could divine, she told Scylla to create a rainbow of light through which she was to pass to the other side.

Though unconscious, the young girl did as she was told, and her spirit lifted and flowed over a misty river to a land of flora and well-being. Waiting for her was a great Lion, splashing playfully on the banks, tumbling about with another creature—a Unicorn. As Scylla reached the other end of the rainbow, the two wonderful creatures bowed enthusiastically then happily embraced her. She did not know how long she played with them but, when they had all rested and the two dozed peacefully along the quiet banks, she kissed each one lightly and closed her eyes. As though not a moment of real time had passed, her spirit gently floated back to her place upon the chaise.

The sorceress smiled and touched the king's hand with reassurance. He turned to the old woman with a tearful eye, but he was surprised to see she had vanished. Turning back to Scylla, his face was all tears as his daughter suddenly opened her eyes and sat up.

"Oh, Father, I have had a wonderful journey. I have been to a place of wondrous rest and ...," she paused. Some how she knew she must speak of it no more. She knew it was to be her secret dream.

She stood and embraced her parents. Glowing, she announced, "Let us go to bed, dear ones. We have a big day for all of us tomorrow, and I am anxious to begin with good speed and healthy mind at the earliest light!"

All bade goodnight and the king walked his beloved daughter to bed, his hand in hers.

—N.C.E

30

The Narwhal

In the northernmost seas a whale exists that is so shy that it is rarely seen, and this is a good thing, because its slender ivory tusk is of legendary value. It was believed that it had special magic power which could enrich its possessor with fame, fortune, and fertility. Often the Narwhal horn was mistaken for a Unicorn horn because of its slender elegance. One could hardly imagine that a Unicorn's horn could be more lovely.

A legend in medieval times told that one could catch a Unicorn by luring it to the lap of a young virgin. The Unicorn was thought not to be able to resist such purity and innocence. Rich men would pay a fortune for the Unicorn's horn. It is believed that he who possesses such a horn by ill means suffers a greater misfortune for that deed than any advantage he thought he might gain by it. Beware of those who display the skins and bones of our vanishing resources, for they know not what they reap.

Happiest are those who respect the right of creatures to roam unharmed in their natural habitats. It is that spirit of freedom that the Unicorn and the Narwhal share. The true treasure we can share with them is to know that their freedom is ours as well.

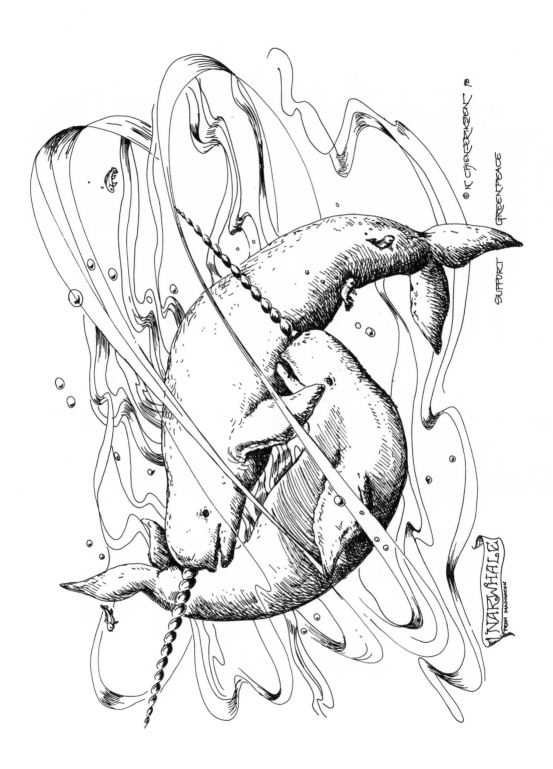

SUPPORT GREENPEACE

© K CHENERKSEN 18

NARWHALE
FROM IMAGINATION

The Fairest of All

A Unicorn walks in its forest content with the tranquility that prevails. So it is everywhere the Unicorn goes. It is the Unicorn's purpose to seek out serenity and beauty. Such a creature comes upon a meadow and sees a young girl sitting among the spring flowers with a majestic lion by her side. The two are obviously companions, for they are relaxed and playful together. The sun highlights her golden hair and his glistening mane.

Normally, the Unicorn would remain in hiding, because he is cautious by nature. He prefers to oversee his kingdom quietly and with modesty. He sees that this is no ordinary maiden, for she frolics with the lion in peace. Surely, he thinks, she has the most peaceful aura of any human he has ever seen. Without hesitating, he approaches.

Seeing the Unicorn, she bows reverently. How she has longed to espy such a wonderful creature. Though she had been told by her countrymen that she herself was the fairest in the land, she herself knew better.

The Unicorn, as is his way, salutes her with a tilt of his horn. She touches it, as all young women aspire to do, but when he is about to leave—for a Unicorn never stays long in one place—she surprises him.

She holds in her hand a flat shiny object, mounted onto a richly designed golden handle, into which she looks with delight. She speaks to the Unicorn saying, "Here I have a likeness of the fairest creature on earth. Lion, what do you think?" Twitching his whiskers the lion purrs in agreement.

"Unicorn, would you like to see, too?" she asks. The Unicorn is tempted. He paws his cloven hoof to signal his curiosity.

"I'll show you, but you must promise me one thing," she tells him. "If you agree that the image you see is the fairest creature you have ever seen, then you must stay with us until the sun retires to bed and the first star takes its place in the twilight sky."

Her invitation is made with such good cheer that he nods his graceful neck in a gesture of agreement. Seeing this, the maiden shows him what is there. The Unicorn expects to see the young girl's image, but to his surprise he does not. It is a white graceful creature with a long slender horn protruding from its head—it is himself! The Unicorn by nature always speaks the truth, and so he stays to play with the maiden and the lion. He no longer wishes to leave because the image in the mirror is truly the Fairest of All.

FAIREST OF ALL

Night Play

What two more delightful creatures
Could there be
Than the Unicorn and Pegasus.

Seen alone,
Either would attract the attention
Of both our eyes and hearts,
But together,
What a scene!

Perhaps late at night
In a hidden forest meadow,
Or on a cushion of stars
Among the constellations,
With the most amazing luck,
We might see them.

The playful Unicorn,
Surefooted and graceful,
Would wrestle and jump,
While Pegasus,
Magnificent and of mighty wing,
Would soar and glide.

They would play in total abandon
...like shooting stars,
For their world is without limit.
The sky is the only boundary
Of their Night Play.

DRAGONS

Graceful,
   Powerful,
      Timeless . . .

Dragons

Throughout history Westerners have depicted the dragon as a fierce and dreaded creature which wreaks havoc and misfortune. In sharp contrast Chinese mythology and art depicts the dragon as a symbol of order and good luck. Nancy is a product of both cultures. Her Chinese heritage has taught her to celebrate the wonderful power of this magnificent creature, knowing too of Western ideas of their so-called evil symbolisms. These dual influences, plus her own personal curiosity, open-mindedness, and love for all animals great and small, have combined to make her vision of the Dragon unique. Her imagination has created a creature that is both magnificent and awe-inspiring. At the same time it is sensitive and volatile, requiring patience and understanding. To her a relationship is possible between the clever but fragile human and the primeval yet responsive beast. The Dragon then becomes a loyal companion.

In a relationship with the Dragon fear becomes trust. Intelligence and love is used to find a way to the heart of the beast. Nancy's dragons dance, roar, fly, romp, and create visions which inspire passion, awe, joy, fear, longing, playfulness, desire, and wonder. The gamut of human emotion appears in her interpretation of dragons. The individual chooses whether or not his or her reaction is the realization of a nightmare—or of a fabulous dream. Denied or embraced, the spirit of the Dragon persists.

© 1976
K. CHIEN-ERIKSEN

Counter Attack

*E*ros never imagined
He would be there that day,
To face the mighty Bezad.
It was the woman, Jennifer
That drew him there.

Part magic, part love,
She stripped him of fear,
But not of his senses.
The power she gave him
Was to be
What he was...

Swift like a horse,
Graceful as a bird,
And clever as a wizard.

Eros outsmarted,
Taunted, and teased the dragon
And turned its rage
Back unto itself,
Until the weight of its greed
Brought its chaotic world
Down upon it.

The most cherished reward
Was not the fame
Or fortune won,
But Jennifer's enchantment
Which gave him...

The daring of an eagle
Freedom of a Centaur
And the spirit
Of a Unicorn.

43

The Seven Headed Dragon

The most unpredictable
And dreaded foe
Of those who would trespass
Towards coveted treasure
Are seven errant minds
Quarrelling, siblings tied together
By fate.
Preoccupied
Among themselves
But united
Against any foe…

Who would dare
intrude
From the outside
On the privacy
Of their domestic chaos…
And attract
The multiple rage
Of the Seven Headed Dragon.

The Collector

Once in a kingdom beyond the edge,
Lived a dragon and his master.
This dragon had a habit.
He collected cities.
Ramus was called the master,
But in reality
If he wanted to keep
His rooms of gold and jewels full
He had to keep his one and only subject
Happy....
And that took whole
Castles, towns and church's riches.
If one only knew of dragons
Like the Collector,
One would certainly hate them.
Everyone in this kingdom did....
Experience was the teacher.
The Collector didn't start out so mean.
More like an overzealous puppy,
Eager to please,
Until Ramus taught him
And tinged his simple mind
With greed.
And now no one
Can stop the Collector,
Not even Ramus.
The master is now a slave
To his own creation.
When you train your dragon....
Watch out!
You may get
What you ask for.

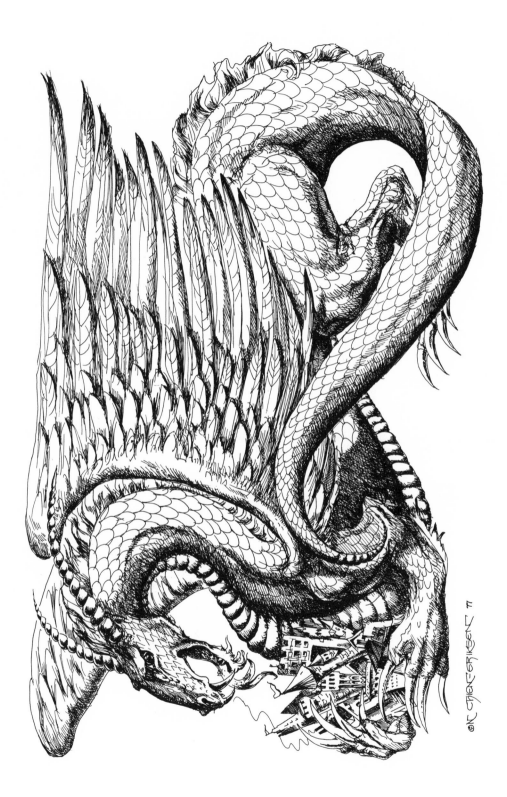

The Prize

The dragon of the air meets his near-match in the tiger, a land-based creature of solitary prowess. Both vie for the capture of the precious sphere—the pearl of universal perfection and value representing infinity and totality at once. Because we all enter into everyday struggles for perfection and achievement, confrontation becomes timeless in itself as a very part of life…even an inspiration.

So it is that our inner and outer conflicts, with their hard-earned resolutions, make life shine truly worthy.

—N.C.E.

© K. CHENCERIKSEN '77

49

Night Flight

In the night sky,
Gentle maidens,
Nymphettes all,
Float in tangent
To their most beloved pride.
Coiled in endless spirals
Of scaled smooth skin
Over rippling sinuous flesh
They glide,
Clinging in delicate balance
With the effortless movement
Of their souls.
Trails of cloth shimmer behind
Amid fragrant strands of hair.
The stars' light
Guides those who know
No earthly bounds,
Forever,
On their timeless quest,
For infinity.

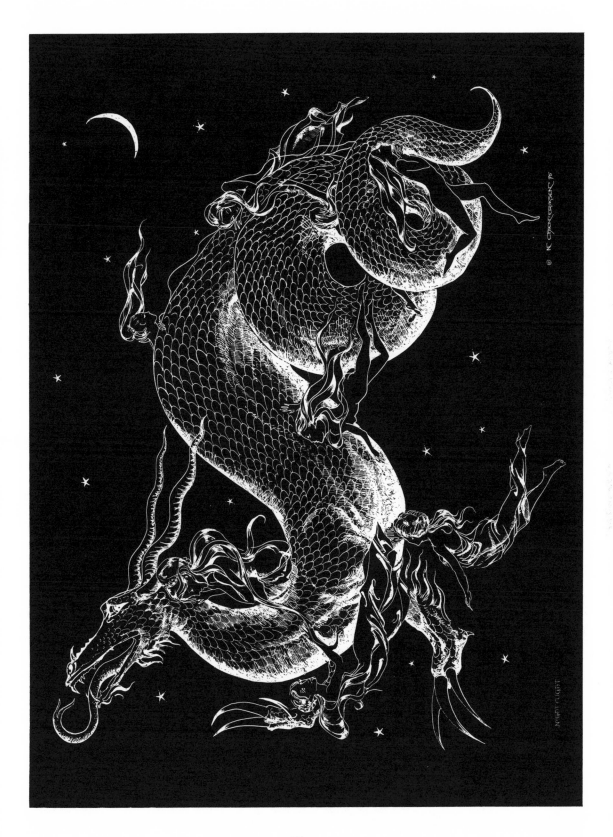

51

The Fuming Dragon

Fire in its eyes
And flames on its breath,
The dragon guards the pearl.
Symbol of the earth,
And all things known
To be precious
And worth defending,
The beast grips the sphere,
Talons extended,
Cautious of anyone
Who might challenge
Its sovereignty.
It stands fast,
Because the world
Is more than a toy
To the Fuming Dragon.

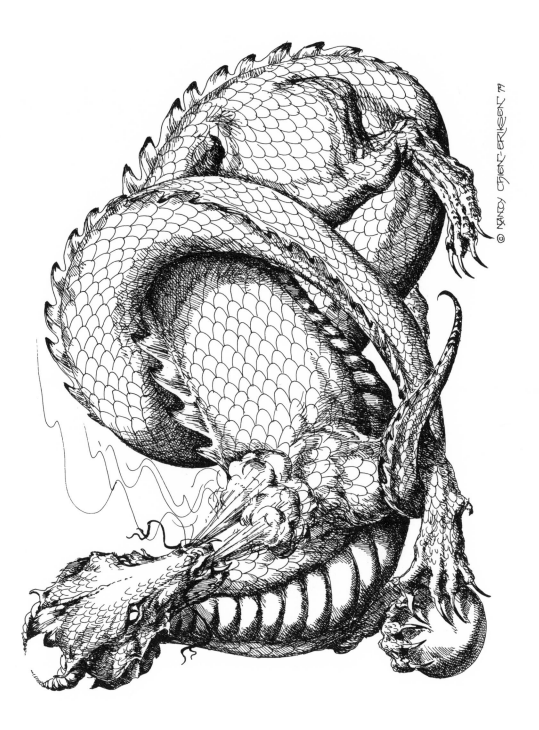

Dragon Guide

The dragon is proud
To bear his master,
Who is so kind ....
Sensitive
To his every move.
She rides between his mighty wings
Whose sweeping strokes
Rise and fall upon the wind
And soothe earthbound cares.

In flight
Only the clouds,
The sky,
And freedom exist
For The Dragon and his Guide.

The Dragon Mistress

It was so small and naked to the world. At first Ileana didn't think it was beautiful, but it was motherless and abandoned. The tiny eyes looked to her as a creature in need of love. She named him Oren. To keep him, she had to find a place to hide him and sneak him food. Her kinfolk had no love of dragons. It was an new adventure.

Rapidly he became strong and curious. Soon he would want fly over the countryside. It was time for her to announce her secret. But when she did, her father didn't believe her and the town elder called her insane. The old shaman woman thought her brash to imagine such a vision. They all thought her too young.

The mayor said, "A dragon your pet? This girl is daft! She should be restrained, for her own good of course." Even her mother cried in confusion and shame.

"I'll prove it to you, then we shall see who is daft," Ileana declared. "I must put a stop to this!" "They must know that I speak the truth." Before anyone could stop her. She ran swiftly into the woods. At last, when she reached her beloved dragon who awaited his beloved master, she said, "We must show them that you are real and good."

Oren was distressed by her agitation. He puffed himself up before the gathering crowd ready to protect his beloved master. Ileana watched him with pride. He remembered all that she had taught him. "It is time!" she announced and climbed between his wings. She grabbed his mane and shouted, "To the sky! Now the world will see how wonderful you are!"

Far below she heard screams of disbelief. The townspeople scattered in panic from the flying dragon. She called down to them, "Please believe me. You need not fear him. Oren only wants to protect me and you if you'll love him." Ileana saw how they all stared up at her and Oren in apprehensive awe. No one had ever taken her seriously before. They must know that she would never hurt her family and friends. Seeing that Ileana was no longer in danger, Oren relaxed. When the townspeople saw that she spoke the truth they gathered in the town hall and she was officially declared Dragon Mistress, and Oren was named City Guardian.

But this story does not end here. It was just the beginning. What had been feared the most became a blessing. Townships and kingdoms from all around came to visit the creature, bringing with them their trade and goodwill. The town prospered.

And Ileana...she became renown for her way with dragons. Dragon pups from as far as across the seas were brought for her care and training. Her unconditional love and patience was observed and practiced throughout the land. She became known as the Dragon Mistress of Langrin.

The Night Conqueror

There once was a land where all of the people feared a mysterious dragon. It roamed unpredictably about the countryside—strangely always at night. The stories of the dragon came to be more immense than its own looming silhouette.

One day a young stranger arrived in the town where the king had promised great rewards to anyone who could destroy or control the lurking beast. No one had even tried in many years, for the unknown had turned to fear and superstition. The young horseman decided to take on the challenge, waiting only until nightfall to make his move.

The horse and rider set out on a new moon with only his spear and his courage. For three nights he encountered nothing but deer and hooting owls. Finally, on the fourth night, he noticed that there was not a sound whatsoever of the usually busy wildlife of the dark. No frogs, no crickets, no calling birds. All was silent. He waited. His horse became uneasy, tossing his head and pawing to move.

Suddenly a tremendous blackness, greater than a mountain, appeared with a rumbling of the earth. Slowly, he saw two enormous eyes begin to glow brighter and brighter, while the dragon's lizard-like scales too began to light and glisten against the black night. His horror was beyond words, he froze nearly stiff.

It was his horse panicking that brought his mind back to his intent. The lad thrust out his spear, but it was a mere cactus spine against an unearthly ship. Suddenly there was a rush of cold, cold wind, and he realized he was being lifted from the ground towards the frightening eye—horse and all. A desperate cry poured from his throat, but he heard only the dragon's roaring breath.

For a reason he himself could not understand, he began calling out to the dragon, and suddenly the young man perceived a strange hollow voice in his mind.

"I am not at war with your kind," said the beast. "You need not fear. I am here because I have always been here, just as the earth was here before you. You men fear me as you fear the night, but you need fear only what you are to yourselves."

"Then what do you want of the people in the town? Why do they want to destroy you?"

"They want power. Whoever removes me thinks he shall be immortal. It is only how they think that limits them. They can co-exist with me just as Man must co-exist with the earth. They do not need to destroy to win."

The dragon slowly lowered the horse and rider to the ground. The young man, as if in an other-worldly dream, dismounted and walked to an ancient olive tree. He pulled off a branch of silver green leaves and, kneeling with his head lowered, offered it humbly to the towering dragon.

"Oh wise one, please accept this symbol of peace from my kind, and let it be a token of understanding. My mission shall be to perpetuate this knowledge. You are no enemy. Perhaps it is only we ourselves."

And, in so speaking, the young man raised his head, only to see the shimmering monster fade silently into the darkness. He saw only a black form against the starry sky, its sparkling eyes becoming like two lost stars among millions. The olive branch was nowhere to be seen.

He knew that in making his peace—in understanding—he had not been defeated but had become a conqueror of the Darkness. He knew clearly now that he must become a conqueror of ignorance.

—N.C.E.

OTHER REALITIES

Joyful,
   Harmonious,
      and Alive . . .

Other Realities

What is fantastic in our waking reality may be ordinary in our imagination. Nancy recreates these other realities in a way that brings them into plain view. To talk and write about them is one thing, but to show them is another, especially when that illustration captures the essence of a dream.

Nancy's resourcefulness becomes apparent when the variety of her work is examined. She goes beyond the obvious. A relationship is formed between the viewer and the viewed. There are many cues from the way a person or creature stands, and the expression on his face says more than his words. In the illustrations that follow Nancy continues to share her visions with us, and the result is that we too are given an opportunity to become visionaries.

The Awakening

She was lost and forlorn and had spent the night on the damp cold ground. Her fears had been amplified by the noises in the night which scurried all about her. When her weariness overtook her she finally slept. In her slumber she dreamed of another time when she felt safe and happy.

Then to her surprise, when she awoke, her eyes opened to behold tall elegant trees in a protective forest where suddenly rays of sunlight beamed between the branches bestowing the warmth of the morning on her tired body. Freshness befell her when she stretched out her arms and embraced the sun's gift openly without restraint.

But as she stretched she felt more than arms and hands. Her skin felt electric as she discovered tremendous wings instead—magical wings that gave her a wind-shaking sense of new freedom to do what she needed to do, to go where she must. Her yearning and her self-determination had granted wings to her, but was she ready for such a change?

The sun rose higher and bathed her. Suddenly she felt at peace with the flowers that welcomed the light and with all the creatures that thrived there. A new feeling came over her, from deep within: it was the warmth of belonging, it was oneness.

The world was no longer foreign or hostile. Her ability to appreciate and to love flowed from the center of her being. The contents of her soul ushered forth in thanks for the gift of her awakening and, at last, with a smile she took to the air.

—N.C.E.

Wind Dancer

On land the horse has captured the heart and companionship of Man. In awe of its swift gallop, and touched by its dedicated loyalty, we have the fortune of having the horse accompany us into the twentieth century as the noblest of friends. How could there be an improvement on such a magnificent creature?

Pegasus!
The one who prances on the land
With ultimate grace,
And glides on the wind
And extends the pulse of its gallop
Into the beat of its wings.

Its mighty feather-endowed limbs
Extend magnificently to each side
And powerfully stroke
Over, through, and beyond
The sea of clouds
That blanket the earth.

And we, though landbound,
Would not be jealous of this creation,
But stand in awe,
With a wish to be swept away
On a flight between the wings
Of the Wind Dancer.

©N CHIEN-ERIKSEN 81

The Wizard

We might suspect
His robe is composed of velvet,
But even velvet is not as deep
As the night sky.
He wears symbols about him
As ornaments
That remind us it is he,
Who with the wave of his staff
And an exuberant incantation,
Can convince all observers
That reality is not what it seems.

Time is not always forwards,
But also backwards
And inside out,
Or not at all.
Matter is no longer solid
But in constant change,
And thoughts are harder than stone.
With one foot in
And one foot out
He visits our world.

It is illusion
We think,
But in our heart
We know that he knows
That we will never know
The secret—unless
We are willing
To give up this world's reality.
He has found out
What we only dream to know.

He is wise
Because he has been here before
And also here after.
He uses what is there,
What we cannot see,
To produce a result
That we think is there.
He knows firsthand that the world,
As hard as it seems,
Is really elastic.
With practiced moves
And studied words
He restores
The magic
To our universe.

The Sorceress

The forces within the Sorceress, like air and land, seek an alliance. The obvious is never enough. She dares to know and use the truth —not just define it. Her staff of fire lights the way through the darkness of illusion, and she renounces the countless doubts that have left all the fearful behind. Many are jealous of her wisdom and suspect her miraculous feats. But the suspicions of those who are petty are but a trifle to her.

Her incantations and herbal potions do not defy logic. They require it. Her interpretations of the past and prophecies of the future do not ignore reason —they use it. Her arms are open to the truth and her wit defies ignorance. The mystery that she commands is empowered by the trust she has in her intuition. Mother Nature, the Goddess of Creation, speaks through her. Her heart is filled with the wonder of the universal fabric that binds life together in an inextricable evolutionary ball of heavenly matter.

The Griffin

*S*o sharp of eye and keen in strength,
Of eagle's breadth and lion's length,
The Griffin soars to guard unguiled
The needs of other creatures wild.

What call is this that now he hears,
A fearful cry—first far, now near.
Below the trees he spies a white
Young unicorn in painful plight.

Its hoof in sprain, it cannot walk,
Yet o'er the rise hears hunters stalk.
With nets of rope and spears they threaten,
From mankind t'is no more hidden.

With hue and cry the men do rush,
"Our prey at last we now can flush!"
Then, ho, just as the net is thrown,
Comes wind of claws and feathers blown.

Twelve hunters shriek in dust to blind,
The Griffin then flies up behind.
Within great claws held gently to,
The Unicorn hangs—now flying too!

Far from the dangerous woods they glide
Then settle on a mountain side.
The Griffin bows then bids request,
"Young Unicorns must do their best"

"To hide from man, for life—not hate,
Captivity is not your fate.
So mind these words, heal and grow,
Your freedom is my noble goal."

The lion beast then leapt on high
With eagle wings devouring sky,
Into the rising sun ensued
So vanished, leaving Hope renewed.

—N.C.E.

The Mermaid

Her long flowing hair
Lies on the sea
Like a fine blanket
Of soft silk.

Below
The long flowing fan of her tail
Shimmers among the kelp.
Her beauty is
Translucent and clear.

If touched or grasped
The pleasure of her vision
Would burst
And disappear
In a mist.

She is a waking fantasy
Existing at the boundary
Between earth and sea,
Where she lives
As a wish
Hoped to be.

The Sea Horse
(Hippocampus)

The horse and the fish are perfect candidates to combine into a universal symbol of the reliance we have on both the land and the sea.

Deep in the vastness of the sea,
Neptune
And his Mermaid companions
Ride the faithful Seahorse.

Swift of hoof and fin
They glide together
Above the stone pathways
And watery gardens
Of blue and green.

Amid showers of minnows
And myrids of shrimp
They mingle
With octopus and eel.

Between the mollusk-encrusted walls
Atlantis
Lies in decay,
And gives up
Its barnacled treasures
To the sea
And to the lovely
Hippocampi.

© N. CHIEN-ERIKSEN 77

Pan

Have you heard the music in the forest? The wind through the branches and the rustle of the leaves combine in a harmony that enchants even the most preoccupied mind. The most captivating of all sounds are the breathy haunting melodies which whisper through hollowed stalks of bamboo. The notes dance and entrance, inviting you to seek their source. You are compelled to follow the hypnotic rise and fall of their line. Mesmerized you forget any once important duty of the day. All you want to do is to dance.

It is a melody which enchants you to stay. Your responsible self says that you should return, for there are practical things to do and to save. But another self rises and says, "Dance to the music of your neglected youth, and yield to the passion of your senses. Succumb to the plea to play like nymphs and satyrs, who pass the days without worry. Listen to the pipes of your long lost ancestor, and this and everyday shall be a special day to dance to the pipes of Pan."

Edition of 150

The Question

They have played for hours
Beneath the tall majestic pines.
And they have chased
Through the open meadows
Among irises in bloom.
All care
Has flown with the breeze,
And worry
Has dissolved into the air.
Their laughter
Has filled the air
With joyousness
And the sun
Has caressed their hair.
Then,
In a moment's pause,
His eyes meet hers
And he leans forward to ask
The question.

81

The Centaur

The essence
of
horse and man.

THE CENTAUR...   © NANCY CHIEN-ERIKSEN '77

The Dance of Life

With first hint of music
We see forms appear.
With each movement
And every turn
The shapes solidify.
Arms, legs, hands, and feet
Define the space
As our eyes and ears become tuned
To every nuance.

This moment of movement
Invites our imagination
To join the performance.
It is an offering
On the altar of life,
An invitation
For us to shed our restraints,
And extend
Our outstretched limbs
From our hearts
Using trust
As our ally
In the dance of life.

—B.C.E.

Rhythm
Harmony
Mood
In this dance we partake.
Life encircles us, yet we are apart.
We are two.
We are one.
We are all
That we need to be what we dream
And that dream becomes us.
Love is our music
As the heart beats the time
And Joy is the Dance of life.

—N.C.E.

© N. Chien-Eriksen '79

The Stream

The water flows gently
With just enough motion
To remain clear and fresh.
A touch sends rings of ripples
Across the the transparent blanket
Which covers the timeworn stones below.

Forever changing
Yet always the same,
The coolness provides tingling relief
From the heat of the day,
And penetrates through tired muscles,
Soothing and dissolving weariness.

Contagious,
The relief spreads
Throughout the entire body,
Until even the mind
Is at peace.

The Pearl

The young fairy often found beautiful stones on the bottom of her favorite bathing place, but this was the most precious. At first she did not believe it was what it was. It was larger than any other she had seen before. Regardless of its enormous size, its pinkish white surface was perfect. It was a magnificent pearl.

The oyster it came from must have been huge. "It must have been cultured by a god for a goddess," she said to the fish and insects busy around her. She could feel the strange power in the object as she held it. "I wonder if it was hidden or lost here? Could it be an accident that it was left here?"

She thought for a moment and then decided, "If this was meant for me, it will still be here when I return. If not, then it was not to be." Before carefully placing it back in its resting place she made a simple wish. She asked that a poor family she knew should come to a better fate. They were kind and hard working, but they suffered terribly for their poverty. As she spoke the pearl seemed to give off a momentary glow. She blinked unsure of what she saw and returned the sphere to its watery place.

On her return she passed the home of the unfortunate family. Lo and behold, they greeted her excitedly with a news of a surprise inheritance from a distant relative. The sum of money was large enough to pay their debts and to buy their land from their proprietor. It was true…it was a pearl of good luck!

When she returned to its resting place once more, the pearl was still there. She resolved to keep it where she had found it, safe from the sight of jealousy and greed. And for as long as it remained there, she used it joyfully to bring a turn of fortune not for herself but for those she knew to be worthy.

A Timeless Moment

In the still warm air
Only an occassional breeze
Stirs the blossoming plants.
She raises her hand
And cautions her impetuous friend
Not to devour
The electric feeling.
She feels harmony and power
Within herself
And wishes not
To break the spell of
This timeless moment.

Lovers' Lair

At the foot of the falls he came to a clear pool fed by rushing falls and surrounded by lush green flora. He thought to himself, what a pity I am alone here among all of this beauty. I wish I could share it with someone. The sun had caused a reflection on the pool, so he gazed into his own image which looked back with curious eyes. He noticed a small butterfly flit to and fro, then land upon a nearby stone.

At that very moment another face appeared next to his in the reflection. It was a beautiful face. She winked, and the wink started the pond to ripple. To see if she were really there, he turned, half expecting her to vanish like an hallucination, but instead she remained.

Her hair was long and flowing, and her skin was rosy and clear. He gasped because behind her, impossible but true, she had two gossamer wings that fluttered like diaphanous rainbows.

Suddenly, she turned away, timid yet beckoning. He smiled and relaxed. With soft words she spoke of his love for this hidden garden. He described his desire to share his little world, for he was overflowing with love.

The fairy butterfly caressed his shoulder and lay back upon the cool moss. His fingers played with her magical tresses. Then she said to him:

"You are a sincere and honest human. Such traits are not to be lost no matter where your path takes you. I am here to encourage your love of yourself and for your fellow humans. I am but a butterfly, yet I shall light upon your shoulder at your first call, to bring you good countenance. I am to be your inner love, your inner spirit. ..if it be your wish."

With grateful tears in his eyes the young man consented. The magic of her words entered him and he was complete. The enchanted lair became forever his, no matter where he would go, for this love was part of him now.

—B.C.E. & N.C.E.

92

Eye of The Beholder

The eyes...
They penetrate.
They look inside
And cause a feeling
That was never there before.

Is this the look of the Unicorn
Or the magical flying horse?
Their gaze conjures visions
Of stirring ancient myths
Revealing
The intensity and intuition
In life.

You walk away,
But the eyes
Only draw you back
To say
That life itself
Is in
The Eye Of the Beholder.

NANCY CHIEN-ERIKSEN '84 ©

For further information about
Nancy Chien-Eriksen prints
and originals, write to
Wind Dance Publications
113 Rice Lane
Larkspur, CA 94939
415 + 924-6049